The
BATHROOM FOOTBALL BOOK

——— • ———

Jeff Kreismer

RED-LETTER PRESS, INC.
Saddle River, New Jersey

THE BATHROOM FOOTBALL BOOK
COPYRIGHT ©2009 Red-Letter Press, Inc.
ISBN-10: 1-60387-116-0
ISBN-13: 978-1-60387-116-7

Red-Letter Press, Inc.
P.O. Box 393
Saddle River, NJ 07458

www.Red-LetterPress.com

ACKNOWLEDGMENTS

EDITORIAL:
Jack Kreismer

•

TYPOGRAPHY:
Matt Taets

•

COVER:
Cliff Behum

•

LAVATORIAL STAFF:
Kobus Reyneke
Lori Walsh

The
BATHROOM
FOOTBALL
BOOK

——— • ———

TAILGATING TRIVIA

The Rose Bowl originated as merely a side attraction to enhance the Pasadena Valley Hunt Club's "Tournament of Roses." The event was held as a showcase for Westerners to show off their fruitful flowers and oranges to people from the East Coast, who endured barren, harsh winters.

•

In what many call "The Greatest Game Ever Played," the 1958 NFL Championship between the New York Giants and the Baltimore Colts, Vince Lombardi was the Giants' defensive coordinator and Tom Landry the offensive coordinator.

•

Joe Gibbs led the Redskins to three Super Bowls with three different starting quarterbacks, the only coach to do so. He also took Washington to an NFC Championship Game with a fourth.

•

The 1992 Alabama football team had a freshman kicker whose name recalled a landmark Supreme Court decision, Wade Roe. His middle initial? V.

•

Although the USFL folded after a lack of interest, they did contribute two very important things to today's game: the

*"Nobody in football should be called a genius.
A genius is a guy like Norman Einstein."*
–Joe Theismann

two-point conversion and instant replay, both of which the NFL adopted.

•

Football great Sammy Baugh once threw four touchdown passes for the Washington Redskins and, playing defense, intercepted four Detroit Lions passes in the same game.

•

In 1978, quarterback Scott Bull played in 16 games for the 49ers, threw just one TD pass and had 11 interceptions for a meager 24.8 rating. The next year, San Francisco drafted Joe Montana.

•

The 1995 Pittsburgh Steelers are the only team to lose a game to a first-year expansion team and still go on to a Super Bowl. They lost to the Jacksonville Jaguars in the Jags' inaugural year, 20-16.

•

Weeb Ewbank is the only coach to win titles in both the AFL and NFL. He won NFL titles in 1958 and 1959 with the Colts, and won the Super Bowl with the Jets in 1969.

•

Former Miss America Phyllis George was the first female football commentator on network TV, co-hosting *The*

"This is the greatest country in America."
–Bill Peterson, Florida State coach

NFL Today on CBS in 1975. George went on maternity leave from the program in 1983 and never returned.

•

Penn State's original school colors were black and pink. However, when the baseball team's uniforms faded to white and dark blue, the school adopted the new colors.

•

As a punter on his high school team, Warren Sapp averaged 43.5 yards a kick.

•

No one in the NFL has had ups and downs like Larry Ball. In his seven-year career, the linebacker played on the undefeated 1972 Miami Dolphins (17-0) and the winless 1976 Tampa Bay Buccaneers (0-14).

•

The winning team of the Super Bowl receives 150 rings from the NFL to disperse throughout their organization.

•

In 2004, Jessica Elway made history by becoming the first woman to ever introduce somebody into the Pro Football Hall of Fame- her father.

•

Although he was known more for his contributions to basketball, James Naismith developed the first football helmet.

"The thing that really sealed it was getting chosen to play in an old-timers' game when I hadn't even retired yet."
—Ruben Carter, on why he retired

In 1993, the town of Ismay, Montana changed its name to Joe, Montana, in honor of the Hall of Fame QB.

•

The NFL's All-Star Game, now called the AFC-NFC Pro Bowl, was first held in 1938 at Wrigley Field- in Los Angeles! The stadium was owned by William Wrigley of bubblegum fame and was an exact replica of the friendly confines in Chicago.

•

A man for all seasons- Hank Soar was a fullback for the New York Giants from 1937 to 1946. He coached the Providence Steamrollers of the NBA in 1947-48. In base-ball, he was an umpire in the American League from 1953 to 1973.

•

When George Halas bought the Chicago Staleys he changed the name to the Bears. Halas reasoned that, because football players are generally bigger than baseball players, and one of the city's baseball teams was the Cubs, logically the football team should be the Bears.

> *"Most people have their ligaments and cartilage inside their knees. I have mine on top of my locker."*
> **–Joe Namath**

Despite catching just four passes all season, Max McGee of the Packers scored the first touchdown in Super Bowl history. In Green Bay's win over Kansas City, McGee finished with seven receptions for 138 yards and two scores.

•

A ninth-round draft pick, Johnny Unitas was cut in training camp by the Steelers in 1955. He would spend the year playing semi-pro football for the Bloomfield Rams for $6 a game and working at a construction site until he was discovered by the Colts.

•

The NFL average attendance dropped from 59,824 one week to 16,947 the next when the league used replacement players during the 1987 strike.

•

Since the NFL's first season in 1920, the team with the best regular season record was awarded the league title. But since the Spartans and Bears tied for first in 1932, a playoff game was needed to crown a champion. Due to those circumstances, the NFL Championship Game was born.

"After 12 years, the old butterflies come back. Well, I guess at my age, you can call them moths."
–Franco Harris, about to wind up his career with the Seahawks after 12 years with Pittsburgh

With his celebrity status at its peak from *Monday Night Football*, ABC gave Howard Cosell a crack at his own live variety show in 1975. The show was short-lived and is remembered today only as a trivia question, as its title, *Saturday Night Live*, could not be used by another network until Cosell's program was cancelled.

•

In 1969, in their first playoff game since a stunning Super Bowl III victory, the Jets fell to the Chiefs in the AFL divisional round, 13-6. Joe Namath, the star of the previous year's Super Bowl, was the goat in this game, completing just 14 of his 40 passes for 164 yards and throwing three interceptions in the swirling winds at Shea Stadium.

•

The number 31 had a place on Buffalo's stationary, but not its jerseys. The number was used in team promotions and it wasn't until 1990 that it was given to Bills players on a regular basis.

LAUGH-IN TIME-OUT

Q: What do you call a football player who becomes a born-again Christian?

A: A two-point conversion

PRE-GAME CHATTER

"Opening games make me nervous. To tell you the truth, I'd rather open with our second game."
–John McKay

— • —

"I'm expecting a good season. I don't know why. Just ignorance, I guess."
–Abe Martin, TCU football coach

— • —

"We definitely will be improved this year. Last year we lost ten games. This year we only scheduled nine."
–Ray Jenkins, Montana State coach

— • —

"Scheduling is very important, depending upon whom you play."
–Bo Schembechler

— • —

"I want you guys to pair up in groups of three, and then line up in a circle."
–Florida State football coach Bill Peterson

*"This year we've got Michigan just where we want them.
We don't play them."*
–Lee Corso, while coaching at Indiana

— • —

*"Our game plan is first year, .500 season. Second year, a conference
championship. Third year, undefeated. Fourth, a national championship. And by the fifth year, we'll be on probation, of course."*
–Bear Bryant

— • —

*"I want to gain fifteen hundred or two thousand yards,
whichever comes first."*
–George Rogers

— • —

"Defensively, I think it's important for us to tackle."
**–Karl Mecklenburg, Denver Broncos linebacker, before Super
Bowl XXIV**

— • —

"I gave George Allen an unlimited budget and he exceeded it."
**–Edward B. Williamson, on why he sacked
the Redskins head coach**

"A good defense always beats a good offense, and vice versa."
–Former Eagles coach Joe Kuharic

— • —

*"Men, I want you just thinking of one word all season.
One word and one word only: Super Bowl."*
–Bill Peterson

— • —

*"When you're playing for the national championship, it's not a
matter of life or death. It's more important than that."*
–Duffy Daugherty

— • —

*"The key to the whole business is sincerity.
Once you can fake that, you've got it made."*
–Monte Clark, Detroit Lions coach

— • —

"Leaving."
**–Jim McMahon, Bears quarterback, on his best memory
of Brigham Young University**

*"Gentlemen, it is better to have died as a small boy
than to fumble this football."*
–John Heisman

— • —

"On this team we are all united in a common goal: to keep my job."
–Lou Holtz

— • —

*"The minute you think you've got it made,
disaster is just around the corner."*
–Joe Paterno

— • —

*"If your work is not fired with enthusiasm,
you will be fired- with enthusiasm."*
–Ex-Patriots head coach John Mazur

— • —

*"The thing I like about football is that you don't have
to take a shower to go to work."*
–Jay Hilgenberg, Bears center

"Usually, the team that scores the most points is going to win it."
–John Madden

— • —

"I don't think there's anybody in this organization not focused on the 49ers... I mean Chargers."
–Bill Belichick

— • —

"The thing you cannot forget is that there isn't anything wrong with winning ugly. As a matter of fact, there isn't anything wrong with being ugly – as long as you're successful."
–Lou Holtz

— • —

"When in doubt, punt!"
–John Heisman

— • —

"Son, it looks to me like you're spending too much time on one subject."
–Shelby Metcalf, Texas A&M football and basketball coach, to a player who received four F's and a D

*"There are three important things in life: family,
religion and the Green Bay Packers."*
–Vince Lombardi

— • —

*"Just remember the words of Patrick Henry -
'Kill me or let me live.'"*
–Bill Peterson, Florida State coach

— • —

*"Everyone has some fear. A man who has no fear belongs in
a mental hospital, or on special teams."*
–Walt Michaels

— • —

*"Never worry about missing a field goal. Just blame the holder and
think about kicking the next one."*
–Lou Groza

— • —

"I don't know. I only played there nine years."
**–Former Cowboys running back Walt Garrison, when
asked if Tom Landry ever smiled**

1 ST QUARTER
ABCs & T or F

Multiple Choice

1. Who is the only wide receiver in NFL history to score a touchdown in the 1970s, '80s and '90s?
   A. STEVE LARGENT
   B. JAMES LOFTON
   C. ART MONK

2. In 2005, what running back became the first player in NFL history to score at least 15 touchdowns in five consecutive seasons?
   A. LADAINIAN TOMLINSON
   B. EDGERRIN JAMES
   C. SHAUN ALEXANDER

3. What Major League great set a national high school record with four touchdown returns in a single game in 1951?
   A. ROGER MARIS
   B. HANK AARON
   C. SPARKY ANDERSON

> *"I knew it was time to quit when I was chewing out an official and he walked off the penalty faster than I could keep up with him."*
> **—George Halas, on retiring**

4. What head coach led the Saints to their first-ever playoff win during the 2000 season?

     A. MIKE DITKA

     B. JIM HASLETT

     C. JIM MORA

5. What University of Chicago halfback was the first Heisman Trophy winner in 1935?

     A. JAY BERWANGER

     B. DAVEY O'BRIEN

     C. GLENN DAVIS

6. Who holds the NFL's single-game record for sacks, with 7?

     A. LAWRENCE TAYLOR

     B. DERRICK THOMAS

     C. OSI UMENYIORA

7. The year 2005 marked the first time in twenty seasons that a Browns running back ran for 1,000 yards. Who accomplished the feat?

     A. JAMAL LEWIS

     B. WILLIAM GREEN

     C. REUBEN DROUGHNS

> *"We're not giving away any football players who could hurt us later. I don't mind people thinking I'm stupid, but I don't want to give them any proof."*
> **–Bum Phillips, Houston Oilers coach**

8. Who served as the head coach of both the expansion
   Carolina Panthers and Houston Texans?
      A. GEORGE SEIFERT
      B. JOHN FOX
      C. DOM CAPERS

9. What former NFL receiver played the part of Deacon
   Moss in the 2005 remake of *The Longest Yard*?
      A. MICHAEL IRVIN
      B. JERRY RICE
      C. CRIS CARTER

10. Who's the first player in NFL history to have earned
    Super Bowl rings with three different teams?
       A. CHARLES HALEY
       B. MATT MILLEN
       C. MIKE DITKA

11. Since opening in 2002, what NFL stadium has already
    hosted a Super Bowl (XL) and a college basketball
    Final Four (2009)?
       A. DETROIT'S FORD FIELD
       B. HOUSTON'S RELIANT STADIUM
       C. ARIZONA'S UNIVERSITY OF PHOENIX STADIUM

*"All those college football coaches who hold dressing-room prayers
before a game should be forced to attend church once a week."*
–Duffy Daugherty

12. What Dallas Cowboys defensive lineman was 6-0 as a pro fighter in 1979?
    A. RANDY WHITE
    B. ED "TOO TALL" JONES
    C. HARVEY MARTIN

13. What football personality has been chosen by a record number of Pro Football Hall of Fame inductees to present them at the Canton, Ohio ceremony?
    A. DON SHULA
    B. JERRY JONES
    C. AL DAVIS

14. With 2,544 points, who is the NFL's all-time leading scorer?
    A. GEORGE BLANDA
    B. MORTEN ANDERSEN
    C. JASON ELAM

15. Who was the first player in AFL history to catch 100 passes in a single season?
    A. CHARLEY TAYLOR
    B. LIONEL TAYLOR
    C. LANCE ALWORTH

"Don't blame me. Blame the foursome ahead of me."
–Lawrence Taylor, when late for a Giants practice

16. How many feet wide is a football field?
   A. 125
   B. 160
   C. 200

17. The award given to college football's top defensive back is known as what?
   A. THORPE AWARD
   B. PAYTON AWARD
   C. OUTLAND TROPHY

18. In 2009, who became the first defensive player in NFL history to sign a $100 million contract?
   A. ASANTE SAMUEL
   B. ALBERT HAYNESWORTH
   C. JARED ALLEN

19. What two teams played in the "Ice Bowl", the 1967 NFL Championship Game?
   A. PACKERS AND RAMS
   B. COLTS AND BROWNS
   C. PACKERS AND COWBOYS

"A quarterback doesn't come into his own until he can tell his coach to go to hell."
–Johnny Unitas

20. Who's the all-time leading rusher in the history of the
    Indianapolis Colts?
    A. MARSHALL FAULK
    B. EDGERRIN JAMES
    C. ERIC DICKERSON

THOUGHTS OF THE THRONE

*Hall of Fame quarterback Dan Marino had his
Florida home on the market in 2009 for $13.5
million. The 15,000 square-foot abode has how
many bathrooms? You're not expected to know
that right off the bat, but if we told you it's the
same number as the one most often worn by a
Super Bowl-winning quarterback that might help.
Did it?*

ANSWERS

1.	B
2.	C
3.	A
4.	B
5.	A
6.	B
7.	C
8.	C
9.	A
10.	B
11.	A
12.	B
13.	C
14.	B
15.	B
16.	B
17.	A
18.	B
19.	C
20.	B

"People are needed, but nobody is necessary."
—Paul Brown

True or False

1. Steve Young is the first left-handed quarterback to earn election to the Pro Football Hall of Fame.

2. The Patriots played home games in Fenway Park during the mid-1960s.

3. The score of a forfeited football game is 6-0.

4. The highest-rated *Monday Night Football* telecast was the Miami Dolphins' victory over the previously unbeaten Chicago Bears on December 2, 1985.

5. Reggie White recorded more career sacks as a Green Bay Packer than as a Philadelphia Eagle.

6. NFL head coaches use red flags to signal their challenge of a ruling on the field.

"If winning isn't everything, why do they keep score?"
–Vince Lombardi

7. Chad Ocho Cinco (formerly Chad Johnson) is a cousin of former NFL wide receiver Keyshawn Johnson.

8. The oldest college bowl game is the Orange Bowl.

9. Tom Brady signed with the Patriots as an undrafted rookie free agent in 2000.

10. Home teams for outdoor games must make more NFL game balls available than home teams for indoor games.

11. Father-son QB duo Phil and Chris Simms each led their team to the playoffs in their rookie season in the NFL.

12. Of all head coaches with at least 100 career wins, John Madden has the highest winning percentage.

13. The New York Jets and Cleveland Browns took part in both the first and last *Monday Night Football* game on ABC.

"We are very proud of him. He's our first offensive lineman to ever become President."
—William Perry, on former Michigan Wolverines player Gerald Ford

14. The first touchdown pass of Peyton Manning's career was to Marvin Harrison.

15. The Super Bowl has never gone into overtime.

16. Brett Favre is the NFL's all-time record holder for both touchdown passes and interceptions.

17. The quarterback's exclamation for the football snap stems from "Hut", as in football Hall of Famer Don "Hut"son, whose name was called in so many plays in early Green Bay Packers history.

18. Jerry Rice played his final NFL game as a member of the Oakland Raiders.

19. Football legend Jim Thorpe served as the NFL's first president.

20. Archie, Peyton, and Eli Manning were all #1 overall picks in the NFL Draft.

"It has been my experience that the fastest man on the football field is the quarterback who has just been intercepted."
—Barry Switzer

ANSWERS

1. True
2. True – *Back then, they were the Boston Patriots of the AFL.*
3. False – *It's 2-0.*
4. True
5. False – *White had 124 sacks with Philadelphia and 68.5 with Green Bay.*
6. True
7. True
8. False –*It's the Rose Bowl, first played in 1902.*
9. False – *He was drafted by New England in the sixth round, pick 199 overall.*
10. True – *Home teams for outdoor games must provide 36 game balls. Only 24 are needed for indoor games.*
11. False – *Neither did.*
12. True
13. False – *The Jets played the Browns in the first MNF game in 1970 and played the Patriots in the last game in 2005.*
14. True
15. True
16. True
17. False – *Football historians say that the "hut" stems from Army drills where the sergeant would count off "Hut-2-3-4."*
18. False – *Seattle Seahawks*
19. True
20. False – *Peyton and Eli went #1, but Archie was the second pick in the 1971 NFL Draft.*

"He's a great player. He ceases to amaze me every day."
–Ray Perkins, Tampa Bay
Bucs coach, about kicker Gary Anderson

Whodunit?

1. Who's the first starting quarterback to win two playoff games in his rookie season?

2. In 2004, who recorded the first defensive touchdown in a playoff overtime game in NFL history?

3. Who became the first QB-WR combo in NFL history to hook up for more than 10,000 career yards?

4. In 1982, what Washington Redskin became the first and only kicker to win the NFL MVP Award?

5. In what turned out to be Dan Marino's final NFL game, who defeated the Miami Dolphins 62-7 in the 2000 Divisional Playoffs?

6. In 1983, two future Hall of Famers were selected with

"Jerry Rice is the greatest and I'm the best."
–Wide receiver Andre Rison

the first two picks in the draft. John Elway went number one. Who was drafted second?

7. In 2008, who was named the NFL's Comeback Player of the Year for the second time in just three seasons?

8. Who was named the head coach of the Jets after the 1999 season, only to resign before coaching his first game?

9. The now-defunct XFL produced only one MVP, as it lasted just one season. The recipient would then sign on with the Pittsburgh Steelers. Who was it?

10. Who holds the Broncos' single-season record for passing yards, with 4,526?

11. Who are the only two players to rush for 1,000 yards in each of their first 10 NFL seasons?

12. Can you name the only team to lose 16 games in an NFL season?

"Because if it didn't work out, I didn't want to blow the whole day."
—Paul Hornung, Green Bay Packers running back, when asked why his wedding was held in the morning

13. Whose 235 TD passes were the most by any NFL quarterback during the 1990s?

14. With a 109-yard TD return off a missed field goal in 2007, who is credited with the longest play in NFL history?

15. In 1989, who replaced the legendary Tom Landry to become just the second head coach of the Dallas Cowboys?

16. Who is the only quarterback in NFL history to have six straight seasons with at least 4,000 yards passing?

17. Who was the first African-American elected to the Pro Football Hall of Fame?

18. Who led the Baltimore Ravens to the 2008 AFC Championship Game in his first season as an NFL head coach?

19. In 1977, who became the first football player ever to host *Saturday Night Live*?

"If we didn't have a huddle, Jim would have no social life."
–Phil Simms, on lineman Jim Burt

20. Who was the only player to ever top Jim Brown for the NFL rushing title during Brown's nine seasons in the league?

21. As a rookie in 2003, who set an NFL record for the most receiving yards in his first game, with 217?

22. In sudden death overtime, who scored the winning touchdown in "The Greatest Game Ever Played" between the Colts and Giants in 1958?

23. In 1960, who teamed up with Art Powell to become the first professional wide receiver duo to gain 1,000 yards each in a season?

24. Who was the last defensive player to win the Associated Press NFL MVP Award?

25. Who are the only two NFL players to have played with just one team for two decades?

"I like chocolate cake."
—Quarterback Troy Aikman, when asked if the Dallas Cowboys released him because of the effects of his ten concussions

ANSWERS

1. Joe Flacco, with the Ravens in 2009
2. Al Harris – Harris ran back a Matt Hasselbeck pass 52 yards to give the Packers a 33-27 win over the Seahawks.
3. The Colts' Peyton Manning and Marvin Harrison, in 2005
4. Mark Moseley
5. Jacksonville Jaguars
6. Eric Dickerson
7. Chad Pennington
8. Bill Belichick
9. Tommy Maddox
10. Jay Cutler, in 2008
11. Barry Sanders and Curtis Martin
12. The 2008 Detroit Lions

LAUGH-IN TIME-OUT

Q: What do you call the NFL's out-of-control Baltimore offensive lineman?

A: A Raven lunatic

13. Brett Favre
14. Antonio Cromartie
15. Jimmy Johnson
16. Peyton Manning
17. Emlen Tunnell
18. John Harbaugh
19. Fran Tarkenton
20. Jim Taylor
21. Anquan Boldin
22. Alan Ameche – Baltimore won, 23-17.
23. Don Maynard, of the New York Titans
24. Lawrence Taylor, in 1986
25. Darrell Green, with the Redskins, and Jackie Slater, with the Rams

THOUGHTS OF THE THRONE

This city is unofficially nicknamed the "Toilet Paper Capital of the World." It's also the only city which owns an NFL team.

What city?

Green Bay, Wisconsin

Who Said It?

1. When asked about leaving the USFL for the NFL, this former L.A. Express quarterback explained, "Now we don't have to chip in to pay the bus driver to get us to the airport."

2. When his team was invited to the White House after Super Bowl XLIII, he called out the president: "If you want to see the Pittsburgh Steelers, invite us when we don't win the Super Bowl. As far as I'm concerned, (Obama) would've invited Arizona if they had won."

3. "Even when I was little I was big", said the man whose Super Bowl ring size is the largest of any player in the history of the event.

4. According to this Hall of Fame receiver, "Jimmy Johnson used to tell us, 'Listen, you came to the University of Miami to play football. If you wanted an education, you should have gone to Harvard.'"

> *"Old place-kickers never die. They just go on missing the point."*
> **–Hall of Fame kicker Lou "The Toe" Groza**

5. "It's a humbling thing being humble", said this Ohio State running back after seeing his draft stock diminish in 2005.

6. "I was drafted by the Pittsburgh Steelers in 1970. Now folks...we didn't have a love affair when it started. Y'all called me Ozark Ike 'cause I was big and white and dumb actin'."

7. According to this 13-time Pro Bowl selection, "I feel like I'm the best, but you're not going to get me to say that."

8. This former QB remarked, "I'm not fast. But there are a lot of guys that are a hell of a lot slower than I am. If somebody wants to do a pay-per-view race between me and (Tom) Brady, sign me up."

9. This coach praised one of his best players by saying, "Earl (Campbell) may not be in a class by himself, but whatever class he's in, it doesn't take long to call the roll."

"If my quarterback runs, I'll shoot him."
–Bill Parcells, describing a run and shoot offense

10. The author of the children's book *Little T Learns to Share* once argued, "Don't say I don't get along with my teammates. I just don't get along with some of the guys on the team."

11. "You hear about how many fourth quarter comebacks that a guy has and I think it means a guy screwed up in the first three quarters", said the man who led the largest comeback ever in a conference title game.

12. On his quarterback, Jim McMahon, he explained, "We have a strange and wonderful relationship. He's strange and I'm wonderful."

13. After playing in the NFL, CFL and AFL, he said, "Pro football gave me a great sense of perspective to enter politics. I'd already been booed, cheered, cut, sold, traded and hung in effigy."

14. This former NFL commissioner said, "I'm a firm believer that all sports will eventually be global. Someday, we may have a quarterback from China named Yao Fling."

"How do you know what it's like to be stupid if you've never been smart?"
–Lou Holtz

15. When asked why he never watched *Monday Night Football*, this Jackson State star said, "It makes as much sense as a secretary going home and spending her nights typing."

16. Amidst the Patriots' "Spygate" controversy in 2007, this Charger joked that New England lived by the saying, "If you ain't cheatin', you ain't tryin'."

17. He led the league in passing yards each season from 1979-82. Years later came this proclamation: "Now that I'm retired, I want to say that all defensive linemen are sissies."

18. While reflecting on his 26-year NFL career, this quarterback/placekicker said, "The thing is that by the time I finished playing, I was too old to be starting out as a coach."

19. In 2008, following a 13-13 stalemate with the Bengals, he revealed, "I've never been a part of a tie. I never even knew that was in the rule book."

"If you're a pro coach, NFL stands for 'Not For Long.'"
–Jerry Glanville

20. "When we won the league championship, all the married guys on the club had to thank their wives for putting up with all the stress and strain all season. I had to thank all the single broads in New York."

THOUGHTS OF THE THRONE

True or false? When the Cowboys' new stadium opened in Arlington, Texas, in 2009, it was built to conform to the state's potty parity law, which calls for two women's toilets for every men's toilet.

True. There are 893 toilets for women, 356 for men.

ANSWERS

1. Steve Young
2. James Harrison
3. William "Refrigerator" Perry
4. Michael Irvin
5. Maurice Clarett
6. Terry Bradshaw
7. Jerry Rice
8. Drew Bledsoe
9. Bum Phillips
10. Terrell Owens
11. Peyton Manning, who led the Colts back from 18 down to beat the Patriots in 2007
12. Mike Ditka
13. Jack Kemp
14. Paul Tagliabue
15. Walter Payton
16. LaDainian Tomlinson
17. Dan Fouts
18. George Blanda
19. Donovan McNabb
20. Joe Namath

"Describing Don Shula as intense is like describing the universe as fairly large."
–Dave Barry

Who Am I?

1. As a teenager, I was a ball boy for the Minnesota Vikings. In 2005, I had my first 1,000-yard receiving season in the NFL.

2. I'm the first head coach in NFL history to lead four different teams to the playoffs.

3. With 19,013 combined punt and kickoff return yards in my career, spent mostly with the Redskins, I easily rank as the all-time leader in the category.

4. I won the Heisman Trophy in 2001 but never played a down in the NFL.

5. I led my squad to four consecutive NFC Champion-ship Game appearances in the 2000's.

6. As a quarterback, I didn't start a single game in col-lege. Nevertheless, I was selected by the Patriots in the seventh round of the NFL Draft in 2005.

"When you get hurt, everything hurts- hands, toes, fingers, everything. I can't even play golf. I sound like I'm making popcorn when I get up in the morning."
–Lawrence Taylor, on aging

7. I'm an NBA coaching legend who was the first-ever draft pick of the San Diego Rockets in 1967. The Dallas Cowboys also drafted me that same year as a wide receiver.

8. I'm the first quarterback in NFL history to finish a season with at least 30 TD passes and fewer than 10 interceptions.

9. I am the only man to coach a team in the Super Bowl and to play on an NBA championship team.

10. Years after going undrafted, I was named the 2008 AP NFL Defensive Player of the Year after recording 16 sacks.

11. I may be known as an NFL linebacker, but in 2009, I began to "Tackle the Globe", hosting a show on the Travel Channel about international sports and culture.

"One of my uncles was a classic paranoid who couldn't sit through a football game. He thought the guys in the huddle were talking about him."
–Sportswriter Franz Lidz

12. In 2004, at the age of 31, I became the oldest player in NFL history to lead the league in rushing, winning the title by one yard over Shaun Alexander.

13. I returned a kickoff or a punt for a touchdown for an NFL-record four consecutive games in 2003.

14. I was inducted into the Pro Football Hall of Fame as a player in 1998. Ten years later, I became the head coach of the 49ers.

15. In 2005, I set an NFL record with three consecutive 100-yard rushing performances to start my pro career.

16. I began my career with the expansion Seattle Seahawks and proceeded to lead the team in receiving for twelve years in a row.

17. In 1981, I caught a 90-yard touchdown pass from Terry Bradshaw for the longest passing play in Steelers' history. It was the only reception of my career.

"I looked in the mirror one day and I said to my wife, 'How many great coaches do you think there are?' She said, 'One less than you think.'"
–Penn State football coaching icon Joe Paterno

18. My days as an NFL quarterback were spent backing up John Elway. Then, after serving as Denver's offensive coordinator, I became the head coach of the Houston Texans in 2006.

19. At the age of 31, I was the oldest rookie in NFL history to make an opening day roster, with the Jets in 2005.

20. As a defensive coordinator, I was the architect of the 46 Defense, which played a huge role in bringing the Bears the 1985 NFL title.

21. Despite being a seventh round draft pick in 2006, I gained 1,000 yards receiving in each of my first two NFL seasons.

22. I recorded double-digit sacks in each of the first four years of my career (2002-05), peaking at 16 sacks in 2004.

"I'm glad we're not going to the Gator Bowl."
–Lou Holtz, after fans pelted his team with oranges upon their Orange Bowl invitation

23. In 2002, I broke my own record of the oldest NFL player to record over 1,000 receiving yards in a season.

24. In 2004, I became the first Patriot to have a reception and an interception in the same game.

25. I may be best known as a Pro Bowl defensive end, but I also hold a rare distinction of playing in both the NCAA men's basketball Final Four and the Super Bowl.

THOUGHTS OF THE THRONE

A stand-up kind of guy, what former Patriots/Jets running back showed off his personal urinal on MTV's "Cribs" (recommending it to all men, so their wives won't bug them about putting down the seat)?

Curtis Martin

ANSWERS

1. Larry Fitzgerald
2. Bill Parcells, with the Giants, Patriots, Jets and Cowboys
3. Brian Mitchell
4. Eric Crouch
5. Andy Reid, with the Philadelphia Eagles
6. USC's Matt Cassel (now with the Chiefs)
7. Pat Riley
8. Donovan McNabb, with 31 TDs and just 8 INTs in 2004
9. Bud Grant, who coached the Minnesota Vikings and played on the 1950 Minneapolis Lakers
10. James Harrison
11. Dhani Jones (*Dhani Tackles the Globe*)
12. Curtis Martin, with 1,697 yards
13. Dante Hall
14. Mike Singletary
15. Carnell "Cadillac" Williams

"If the rest of Washington ran as efficiently as this football team, there wouldn't be any deficit."
–Jeff Bostic, describing the Redskins

16. Steve Largent
17. Mark Malone
18. Gary Kubiak
19. Ben Graham
20. Buddy Ryan
21. Marques Colston
22. Dwight Freeney
23. Jerry Rice, at age 40
24. Troy Brown
25. Julius Peppers, who played football and basketball at the University of North Carolina

THOUGHTS OF THE THRONE

National Bathroom Reading Week is an annual movement celebrated in the first week of June. It was also in the first week of June 1990 when the Big Ten admitted an eleventh member, a storied institution that has won four National Championships.

Can you name it?

Penn State

HALFTIME

Laugh-in Time-out

Terrell Owens, Tom Brady and Jerry Rice are standing before God at the Pearly Gates. The Lord looks at them and says, "Before I grant you a place at my side, I must first ask you what you believe in." He asks Brady, "What is it that you believe?"

The Patriots quarterback looks at God and says with great passion, "I've been a Super Bowl winner more than once and I believe I have brought great joy to the fans of New England as a result. I believe in good sportsmanship on the field at all times and I think I've done that. More importantly, I believe one needs a strong sense of morals and values off the field and I would hope you think I've exhibited that, God."

"That I do, Mr. Brady. Take the seat to my left... And you, Mr. Rice?"

"Well, Lord, you know all things. You're well aware of the many records I set, primarily due to the fact I've always kept in the greatest shape possible. Indeed, I believe in keeping the body and mind as sound as possible."

"That you've done, Mr. Rice. I'm proud of you. You may

"But the real tragedy was that 15 hadn't been colored yet."
—Steve Spurrier, Florida football coach, telling Gator fans in 1991 that a fire at Auburn's football dorm had destroyed 20 books

take the seat to my right... And you, Mr. Owens. What do you believe?"

"I believe you're in my seat."

•

Little Johnny was in his kindergarten class when the teacher asked the kids what their dads did for a living. The usual jobs came up- fireman, salesman, accountant, policeman- but Johnny was uncharacteristically shy about giving an answer. Finally, the teacher said, "Johnny, how about you? What does your father do for a living?"

Johnny murmured, "My dad's an exotic dancer."

The startled teacher quickly ended that segment of class and sent the other kids off to do some coloring. Then she took little Johnny aside and said, "Is that really true about your father?"

"No", said Johnny, "He plays for the Detroit Lions, but I was too embarrassed to say it."

"There were 150 people in the courtroom- third largest crowd ever to see the USFL in action."
—David Letterman, on the USFL antitrust lawsuit against the NFL

A guy comes home from work, plops himself onto the Barcalounger in the family room, grabs the remote, and flips on the football game on the big screen HDTV. He yells into the kitchen, "Honey, bring me a cold one before it starts."

His wife brings him a can of beer. A few minutes later, he calls out to the wife again, "Honey, bring me another beer before it starts."

Again, his wife brings him a beer. A short time later, he yells a third time, "Honey, bring me another beer before it starts."

The wife, now exasperated, marches into the family room and says, "You bum. I've been doing the wash...the dishes...the ironing...and now I'm waiting on you hand and foot!"

The husband says, "Oh, my God! It's started already!"

•

A Jewish football player received a scholarship to Notre Dame. When there was a semester break, he flew home. His rabbi bumped into him at the airport. Aware that the player was a member of the Fighting Irish football team

> "It's like standing blindfolded in the middle of Interstate 75, dodging the cars and trying to tackle the biggest truck out there."
> —Gary Burley, on trying to take down Earl Campbell

the rabbi said, "Tell me, son. They haven't converted you to their ways, have they?"

The football star answered, "Why, no...absolutely not, Father!"

•

Muggsy and Buggsy had been together in Hell for many, many years. Their eternal job was to shovel coal into the fires side by side. Suddenly, one day they felt cold air. The air got colder and colder. Snow began to fall. The next thing they knew, there was a blizzard. The snow blanketed the ground and extinguished the fires. Next, a gust of frigid wind froze over the entire surface of Hell!

"What the heck is going on here?" Muggsy wondered out loud.

Buggsy answered, "I don't know for sure, but I have a hunch that the Bills just won the Super Bowl."

•

After Oakland Raiders owner Al Davis dies and goes to heaven, God is taking him on a tour of the place. He shows Al a small three-bedroom home with a tiny Raiders pennant hanging over the front porch. "This is your

"If talking was an Olympic sport, Theismann is Jim Thorpe."
**—Mike Lupica, writer, about footballer
turned broadcaster Joe Theismann**

eternal home, Al," says God. "You should feel mighty proud because most folks don't get their own private living quarters here."

Al looks at the home, then does an about face and sees this huge four-story mansion with two gigantic Dallas Cowboys flags flying between the four marble pillars. And parked in the circular driveway is a blue and white limo with the Cowboys logo on the hood. "Thanks for my home, God," says Al, "but I have just one question. You give me this tiny home with a miniature Raiders pennant and Jerry Jones gets that beautiful mansion. How come?"

God laughs and says, "Oh, that's not Jerry Jones' home. That's mine."

•

Hall of Fame quarterback Steve Young was once poked in the eye during a pileup. He went to the sideline where the trainer recommended he put on an eye patch. Young felt it might hurt his peripheral vision on one side, so he refused. Before he went back into the game his coach advised him to rely on the peeper that was okay as he said, "Remember, only the good eye, Young."

> *"I kicked six days a week and took*
> *Sunday off- just like I did last season."*
> **–Punter Dave Jennings, after an off-year, explaining his**
> **training camp routine**

There were just six seconds left on the clock of a tied pig-skin contest. The quarterback threw a Hail Mary pass to the first-year wide receiver. He made a spectacular catch, only to be hammered by the opposing cornerback. The ball fell loose and was picked up by a defender who ran the ball all the way for a game-ending touchdown. When the coach was asked about the heartbreaking defeat, he responded, "That's the way the rookie fumbles."

•

A guy desperately wants to go to the Super Bowl so he goes to a scalper, but can get only one ticket. He pays top dollar for a seat in the nose-bleed section, the second to last row of the upper deck. As the game begins, the guy's watching through his binoculars. He notices that there's an empty seat in the very first row, right on the fifty-yard line. As the second quarter is about to end, he looks down and sees that the fifty-yard line seat is still empty. At halftime, he makes his way down to the empty seat and asks the guy who's sitting in the next seat, "Is this taken?"

The guy replies, "No."

"Would you mind if I sit here?"

> *"God is always on the side which has the best football coach."*
> **–Heywood Hale Broun, writer**

The other guy says, "Not at all. Go right ahead."

"I wonder why someone with a front row, fifty-yard line seat wouldn't show up at the Super Bowl," says the first guy.

The second guy says, "Actually, my wife and I have come to every Super Bowl since 1967, but she passed away."

"Oh, gee, I'm sorry to hear that," says the first guy. "But couldn't you get a friend or relative to come to the game?"

"They're all at the funeral."

•

The middle linebacker is calling out the signals. He announces in the huddle that he'll holler out a name beginning with an "e" if it's a run, and a name that starts with "o" if it's a pass. The opposing quarterback sets up over center and is calling an audible. The defensive captain immediately gets a read on it and yells, "Oedipus!"

•

Chargers coach Norv Turner is upset over his team's recent losing streak so he decides to visit Bill Belichick at a New England practice. "Coach, how is it that the Patriots al-

> *"Paul Brown treated his players as if he bought them at an auction with a ring in their noses."*
> **–Jim Murray, columnist**

ways seem to be on a roll? What's your secret?"

Belichick says, "Watch this." He calls over Tom Brady and says, "Tom, who's your father's brother's nephew?"

Brady responds, "That's easy, coach…me."

Belichick looks at Turner and says, "That's what it takes, Norv- a smart quarterback. You've got to have a smart QB."

Turner goes back to San Diego and at the next Chargers' workout calls over Philip Rivers. "Rivers," Turner barks, "Who's your father's brother's nephew?"

Rivers looks baffled, then asks, "Uh, can I get back to you on that, Coach?"

Annoyed, Turner says, "Make it quick."

During practice, Rivers asks LaDainian Tomlinson, "LT, Coach just asked me a strange question: Who's your father's brother's nephew?"

Tomlinson answers, "Duhh, that's simple. It's me."

Later on, Rivers catches up with Turner and says, "Coach, I think I've got it. My father's brother's nephew is LaDainian Tomlinson."

Turner, exasperated, says, "No, no, no… It's Tom Brady!"

"Everybody knows he's coming. It's like a cop putting sirens on his car."
–Beesley Reece, on Lawrence Taylor

3RD QUARTER
Names and Numbers

Names

1. If football's Hall of Famers were listed alphabetically, who would come first?

2. What was the nickname of the defense of the undefeated 1972 Miami Dolphins?

3. In the 2008 NFL Draft, two players with the same last name were selected #1 and #2 overall. Name them.

4. Anthony, a defensive back in the NFL, made two Super Bowl appearances in his career – with the Titans in Super Bowl XXXIV and with the Raiders in Super Bowl XXXVII. Who is his famous football father?

5. What's the real first name of Pro Football Hall of Famer Mean Joe Greene?

LAUGH-IN TIME-OUT

Q: How does Peyton Manning change a light bulb?

A: He passes the job to a receiver.

6. Since joining forces in Minnesota in 2005, these two stud defensive tackles of the same last name have gone on to earn multiple Pro Bowl selections.

7. What college has been referred to as Tailback U because of the great running backs it has produced?

8. In 1986, as a backup to the injured Joe Montana, Jeff threw 11 touchdown passes for the 49ers. His father is the AFL's all-time leading passer. Do you know him?

9. What is the longest standing team nickname in NFL history?

10. Due to a shortage of men gone off to fight in World War II, the Steelers and Eagles merged for the 1943 season. What was their team called?

11. His last name is 14 letters long, and with 112 catches, he was tops in the NFL in receptions in 2007.

> *"There are three types of people...people who make things happen, people who watch things happen and people who don't know what's happening."*
> **–John Madden**

12. The Oilers became the Titans in 1999. Which current NFL team was previously known as the Titans?

13. The last pick in the NFL Draft every year is commonly referred to by what name?

14. Bryan was the first player to win back-to-back Super Bowl MVP awards. By what name do we know him better?

15. Former Patriots running back Craig James teamed with this future Hall of Famer at Southern Methodist University to form the Pony Express backfield.

16. Of all the NFL quarterbacks whose last names begin with the letter Z, who has thrown the most touchdown passes?

17. In the Pro Football Hall of Fame, only two letters of the alphabet are not represented by players' last names. What are they?

"When you're kind of the ugly stepsister, you just go to the prom with whoever asks you."
–Miami Hurricanes coach Larry Coker, on not playing in a BCS bowl

18. His real name is O.A. Phillips, but you can call him Bum. Do you know, though, what his initials stand for?

19. Dan, a quarterback, was the Seahawks' first round pick in 1991. His brother would have a more successful career in Major League Baseball. Can you name the pair?

20. What NFL legend played himself in the 1953 movie titled *Crazylegs: All-American*?

21. This Emmy Award-winning sportscaster and former NFL wide receiver was born Bobby Moore.

22. What team originated as the Decatur Staleys before taking its current name in 1922?

23. This former Raider was known as The Assassin. Who is he?

24. What 1980 squad became known as the Kardiac Kids after many of their games were decided in the final moments?

"Quit coaching? I'd croak in a week."
**–Bear Bryant, who died of a heart attack
a month after retiring**

25. Linguistically speaking, what is wrong with the new last name of Chad Ocho Cinco (nee Johnson)?

26. Edgar, Allan and Poe have all been mascots for what NFL team?

27. Alvin served as the NFL's commissioner from 1960 until 1989. We know him better as…?

28. Can you name the Three Amigos?

29. What Hall of Fame quarterback was nicknamed The Artful Dodger?

30. After the 1921 season, what name was dropped in favor of "National Football League"?

31. In 1998, the Buffalo Bills renamed their stadium this in honor of their owner.

"The man who complains about the way the ball bounces is likely the one who dropped it."
–Lou Holtz

32. This former NFL stadium is known as the Eighth Wonder of the World. Do you know it?

33. What is the name of the trophy awarded to the winner of the Canadian Football League championship?

34. Dimetrios Georgios Synodinos is the real name of what former famous NFL oddsmaker?

35. Nicknamed Bambi, he was the first AFL player to be selected to the Pro Football Hall of Fame.

"You can learn more character on the two-yard line than you can anywhere in life."
–Paul Dietzel, Army coach

ANSWERS

1. Herb Adderley
2. The No Name Defense
3. Jake Long (#1 to Miami) and Chris Long (#2 to St. Louis)
4. Tony Dorsett
5. Charles
6. Pat Williams and Kevin Williams
7. University of Southern California
8. Jack Kemp
9. Green Bay Packers
10. The Steagles
11. T.J. Houshmandzadeh
12. The Jets, in the AFL from 1960-62
13. Mr. Irrelevant
14. Bart Starr
15. Eric Dickerson
16. Jim Zorn, 111
17. Q and X
18. Oail Andrew

---

*"Football isn't a contact sport, it's a collision sport.
Dancing is a contact sport."*
–Vince Lombardi

19. Dan and Mark McGwire
20. Elroy Hirsch
21. Ahmad Rashad
22. Chicago Bears
23. Jack Tatum
24. Cleveland Browns
25. In Spanish, "ocho cinco" simply means "eight five". "Ochenta y cinco" would be the correct way of saying his uniform number of 85 in Spanish.
26. Baltimore Ravens – The team was named after Edgar Allan Poe's poem, *The Raven*.
27. Pete Rozelle
28. Vance Johnson, Ricky Nattiel, and Mark Jackson
29. Roger Staubach
30. The American Professional Football Association
31. Ralph Wilson Stadium (It was originally Rich Stadium.)
32. The Houston Astrodome
33. The Grey Cup
34. Jimmy "The Greek" Snyder
35. Lance Alworth

"I wouldn't ever set out to hurt anyone deliberately unless it was, you know, important- like a league game or something."
–Dick Butkus

Numbers

1. Troy Aikman and Steve Young both wore this number during their Hall of Fame NFL careers.

2. Can you name the NFL team that won a record 18 consecutive road games from 1988-90?

3. When he came into the NFL in 2006, he petitioned the league to wear the #5 from his USC days. After being denied, he now wears #25.

4. Career touchdown passes for Dan Marino: Over or under 400?

5. With a coaching career spanning over 20 years, he's lost the most games in NFL history, 165.

6. He wore the #1 and retired ranking #1 in NFL history in career fumbles, with 161.

> *"I still think the majority of people who vote for the award are like the people in Congress- not very bright."*
> **—Beano Cook, not hiding his dislike for the voters of the Heisman Trophy**

7. His #39 is retired by the Miami Dolphins, where he was a two-time Super Bowl winner.

8. At the snap, the offensive team must have at least how many players on the line of scrimmage?

9. This former Raiders center and Pro Football Hall of Famer wore the number 00 during his career.

10. NFL single-season record for receptions, set by Marvin Harrison in 2002: Over or under 125?

11. How many years must a player be retired to be eligible for election into the Pro Football Hall of Fame?

12. The Seattle Seahawks have retired the #12, but not for a player. What's the reason?

13. With 589, this team broke the NFL record for points scored in a single season, in 2007.

"But now that it's me, it loses some of its mystique."
–Drew Bledsoe, on the aura of being the first overall pick in the NFL Draft

14. What quarterback's 70 pass attempts in a 1994 game vs. the Vikings set an NFL single-game record?

15. Career quarterback rating for Steve Young, the highest in NFL history: Over or under 100?

16. The score was 16-7. The date was January 12, 1969. What happened?

17. This lucky #13 was the first rookie quarterback to be named a starter in the Pro Bowl.

18. With 22.5 sacks in 2001, whose single-season record did Michael Strahan break?

19. Who is the only player to have his number retired by the Buffalo Bills?

20. At the age of 34, who was the youngest inductee into the Pro Football Hall of Fame?

"American football makes rugby look like a Tupperware party."
–Sue Lawley

21. Bruce Smith's NFL record for career sacks: Over or under 250?

22. The record of 47 consecutive games throwing a touchdown pass has stood since 1960. Who holds it?

23. Number of touchdown passes thrown by Kurt Warner in 1999, his first season as a starter: Over or under 35?

24. He's worn the #'s 12, 14, and 16 in his 21-year career, and he's the #1 passer in Tampa Bay history in terms of yardage.

25. Jim Brown and Marcus Allen, who both ran for over 12,000 yards in their careers, wore the same number. What was it?

THOUGHTS OF THE THRONE

"The U.S. Congress can declare war with a simple majority, but we need a three-quarters majority to go to the john."

—Art Modell, Ravens owner, on the difficulty of changing NFL rules

ANSWERS

1. 8
2. San Francisco 49ers
3. Reggie Bush (League regulations restrict running backs to the numbers 20-49.)
4. Over – 420
5. Dan Reeves
6. Warren Moon
7. Larry Csonka
8. 7
9. Jim Otto
10. Over – 143
11. 5
12. It's in honor of the fans, the "12th man".
13. New England Patriots
14. Drew Bledsoe
15. Under – 96.8
16. Joe Namath and the New York Jets pulled off a colossal upset to defeat the Baltimore Colts in Super Bowl III.
17. Dan Marino
18. Mark Gastineau
19. Jim Kelly, #12
20. Gale Sayers, in 1977
21. Under – 200
22. Johnny Unitas
23. Over – 41
24. Vinny Testaverde, with 14,820 yards
25. 32

> *"The only way to stop Jim Brown was to give him a movie contract."*
> **–Spider Lockhart**

4TH QUARTER
Pigskin Potpourri

Pigskin Potpourri

1. In 1985, what former NFL defensive back agreed to have part of his injured finger amputated so that he would not miss a playoff game?

2. Paired with professional dancer Kym Johnson, what former Pro Bowl defensive tackle came in second place on Season 7 of *Dancing With The Stars*?

3. This NFL standout was a college basketball star at Kent State, averaging over 20 points per game in 2003.

4. NFL history was made when 13 players from the same team were selected to the 2008 Pro Bowl. Name the NFC squad.

5. The Cardinals franchise played in what two cities before moving to Arizona in 1988?

"To win, I'd run over Joe's mom too."
–Matt Millen, after hearing Joe Jacoby say, "I'd run over my mother to win the Super Bowl."

6. What three current NFL franchises originated in Cleveland, Ohio?

7. Make the Call: A field goal attempt grazes the helmet of the offensive right guard before it clears the up-rights. Does the field goal count?

8. Since 2006, this London stadium has hosted NFL games in consecutive seasons, as part of the league's International Series.

9. As an NFL head coach, what was the first team Bill Belichick led to the playoffs?

10. In 2009, he became the first head coach to lead the Cardinals franchise to a Super Bowl.

11. What Bengals running back had six consecutive seasons of 1,000 yards rushing from 1997-2002?

"Paul Hornung was an impact player for the Packers. He was also an impact player to half the females in the USA."
–Max McGee, Green Bay wide receiver

12. What NFL team used to play its home games at Wrigley Field?

13. Who was the very first draft pick in Houston Texans history?

14. In 2005, he became the first kicker ever to make 40 field goals in a single NFL season.

15. Make the Call: If a blocked punt goes out of the kicking team's end zone, is it ruled a safety?

16. The origin of what football celebration is credited to former NFL safety LeRoy Butler?

17. This team, founded in 1967, went two decades before having their first winning season.

18. When a referee holds his palms together above his head, what call is he signaling?

---

*"You've heard of people who zig or zag.
Well, Elroy also had a zog and a couple of zugs."*
–Norm Van Brocklin, on Elroy "Crazy Legs" Hirsch

19. Defensive standouts Ray Lewis and Ed Reed both attended what college?

20. The Indianapolis Colts played 24 seasons at this site before moving into Lucas Oil Stadium in 2008.

21. Five NFL teams have bird nicknames. How many can you name?

22. In each of the four seasons before Peyton Manning joined the NFL, what quarterback led the Colts in passing yardage?

23. What former defensive end is credited with coining the term "sack"?

24. For three straight seasons, from 1989-91, Herschel Walker led what team in rushing yardage?

25. Who led the NFL in rushing in 1938 and later became a Supreme Court Justice?

> *"Because John McEnroe never played it."*
> **—Sports columnist Larry Felser, on why
> pro football has become so popular**

26. What former NFL star receiver has a brother who served as the head coach of the NBA's Toronto Raptors?

27. Make the Call: A defensive player intercepts a pass in his own end zone. He attempts to run it out but is tackled in the end zone. What is the ruling?

28. Visitors to the Pro Football Hall of Fame in Canton, Ohio are greeted by a seven-foot bronze statue of what legend?

29. Former Chargers place-kicker Rolf Benirschke pulled a brief stint as host of what TV game show?

30. On November 20, 2005, what two Giants each recorded their 500th career reception?

31. As a linebacker, Jaguars head coach Jack Del Rio was selected to the Pro Bowl in 1994 as a member of what team?

"There is one big difference. You're standing still in golf. Stand still in football and you're dead."
–Hale Irwin, pro golfer and former
University of Colorado defensive back

32. The 2006 football flick *Invincible* is based on the true story of Vince Paple, a 30-year old who earned a spot on what team after coach Dick Vermeil decided to hold open tryouts?

33. In 1976, what team began NFL play by losing its first 26 regular season games?

34. What AFL team's early history included memorable vertically striped socks, which were ultimately burned in a public ceremony?

35. Make the Call: A field goal attempt is blocked and bounces back to the kicker. May the kicker drop-kick it through the uprights?

36. What New Jersey rocker became a founder and majority owner of the Arena Football League's Philadelphia Soul in 2004?

37. Which NFL team switched from the AFC to the NFC in 2002?

"There are no films of irate customers to study."
**—Retired Seahawks receiver Paul Jones, on what
it's like to be a car salesman**

38. Between 1999 and 2001, what two teammates combined to win three NFL MVP Awards?

39. What well-known business mogul was an owner of the USFL's New Jersey Generals?

40. In what decade did the NFL increase its regular season schedule from 14 to 16 games?

LAUGH-IN TIME-OUT

Q: What do you call a Cleveland Browns player wearing a Super Bowl ring?

A: A thief

ANSWERS

1. Ronnie Lott
2. Warren Sapp
3. Antonio Gates
4. Dallas Cowboys
5. Chicago and St. Louis
6. Baltimore Ravens (Cleveland Browns), St. Louis Rams (Cleveland Rams) and Cleveland Browns
7. No
8. Wembley Stadium
9. Cleveland Browns, in 1994
10. Ken Whisenhunt
11. Corey Dillon
12. Chicago Bears
13. David Carr, taken #1 overall in 2002
14. Neil Rackers, with the Cardinals
15. Yes
16. The Lambeau Leap
17. New Orleans Saints
18. Safety
19. University of Miami
20. RCA Dome
21. Cardinals, Falcons, Ravens, Eagles, Seahawks

> *"When I went to Catholic high school in Philadelphia, we just had one coach for football and basketball. He took all of us who turned out and had us run through a forest. The ones who ran into the trees were on the football team."*
> **—George Raveling**

22. Jim Harbaugh
23. Deacon Jones
24. Minnesota Vikings
25. Byron "Whizzer" White
26. Cris Carter, whose brother, Butch, coached Toronto from 1998-2000
27. Touchback
28. Jim Thorpe
29. *Wheel of Fortune*
30. Amani Toomer and Tiki Barber
31. Minnesota Vikings
32. Philadelphia Eagles
33. Tampa Bay Buccaneers
34. Denver Broncos
35. Yes
36. Jon Bon Jovi
37. Seattle Seahawks
38. Marshall Faulk and Kurt Warner, of the St. Louis Rams
39. Donald Trump
40. The 1970's (1978)

> *"It was a very rash statement, and I'd like to apologize to every vulture in the sky."*
> —Former University of Pittsburgh head coach Mike Gottfried, on his statement that every single sports agent is a vulture

SUDDEN DEATH
Killer Trivia

1. In the last twenty years, only one running back has gone #1 overall. Can you name him?

2. In 1997, this San Diego Charger became the first player in NFL history to score on an interception return, fumble return and kickoff return in the same season.

3. What three men made up the original *Monday Night Football* broadcast team?

4. The 2005 NFL Draft marked the first time that two running backs from the same school were picked in the top five. Name the runners, the teams that selected them, and the school they both attended.

5. What team holds the NFL record for the fewest points allowed in a single 16-game season?

6. In 1985, the Cleveland Browns featured two 1,000-yard rushers in a single season. Who were they?

"My knees look like they lost a knife fight with a midget."
–Former Chiefs linebacker E.J. Holubon,
on his 12 knee operations

7. What team did the Tennessee Titans defeat in their stunning playoff win in 2000 that became known as the Music City Miracle?

8. What defensive stud had an NFL-record 358 yards in interception returns in 2004?

9. Only two wide receivers in the last 30 years have won the Heisman Trophy. Name them.

10. Of all quarterbacks, who has the most career rushing TDs in NFL history?

11. For the 2008 season, NFL players wore "GU" on their uniforms. What was the significance?

12. In addition to the Pro Football Hall of Fame, what former NFL owner is a member of the Halls of Fame of National Soccer and International Tennis?

"I like to believe that my best hits border on felonious assault."
–Jack Tatum

13. In 2005, what punter broke Jim Marshall's NFL record of 282 consecutive games played?

14. What is the only team in the NFL without an insignia or logo on its helmets?

15. The sons of Pro Football Hall of Famers Walter Payton and Kellen Winslow Sr. were teammates at what college?

16. What Super Bowl winning head coach played in the same backfield with Floyd Little and Larry Csonka at Syracuse?

17. In 1968, what NFL team became the first to play its home games indoors?

18. In 2005, what country hosted the first NFL regular season game played outside of the United States?

> *"Give that little man just a crease and he's something special. He can stop on a dime and give you nine and a half cents change."*
> **–Nate Newton, on all-time rushing leader Emmitt Smith**

19. Name the three quarterbacks chosen 1-2-3 in the 1999 NFL Draft, the first time this happened since 1971.

20. With 3, what head coach won the most championships in the history of the AFL?

21. This wide out, who was not picked in the 1994 NFL Draft, would become the first undrafted free agent ever to have 10,000 career receiving yards. Do you know him?

22. What two journeymen kickers were named to the NFL's All-Decade Team in both the 1980's and '90's?

23. What Steelers draftee entered the NFL in 2002 as the only Division 1-A player to both throw and run for 40 touchdowns in his college career?

24. What NFL team has had its own volunteer marching band since 1937?

25. Five quarterbacks were chosen before Dan Marino in the 1983 NFL Draft. How many can you name?

*"Religiously speaking, it's an advancement
from a Cardinal to a Saint."*
—**Conrad Dobler, after being traded from St. Louis (then
home of the Cardinals) to New Orleans**

ANSWERS

1. Ki-Jana Carter, selected by the Cincinnati Bengals
2. Rodney Harrison
3. Howard Cosell, Keith Jackson and Don Meredith
4. Ronnie Brown, chosen #2 by Miami, and Carnell Williams, chosen #5 by Tampa Bay, both attended Auburn.
5. Baltimore Ravens - In 2000, they allowed 165 points all season, including 4 shutouts.
6. Earnest Byner and Kevin Mack
7. Buffalo Bills, 22-16
8. Ed Reed
9. Tim Brown (1987) and Desmond Howard (1991)
10. Steve Young, with 43
11. It was a tribute to the late Gene Upshaw, the former head of the NFL Players' Association.
12. Lamar Hunt
13. Jeff Feagles

THOUGHTS OF THE THRONE

According to the Charmin toilet tissue folks, on average, a person uses 57 sheets of toilet paper per day. Would that be more or less than the highest single-team point total in Super Bowl history?

More- The 49ers scored 55 points in Super Bowl XXIV.

14. Cleveland Browns
15. University of Miami (Jarrett Payton and Kellen Winslow Jr.)
16. Tom Coughlin
17. Houston Oilers
18. Mexico – Over 103,000 watched the Cardinals beat the 49ers in Azteca Stadium, Mexico City.
19. Tim Couch, Donovan McNabb and Akili Smith
20. Hank Stram
21. Rod Smith
22. Gary Anderson and Morten Andersen
23. Antwaan Randle El
24. Washington Redskins
25. John Elway, Todd Blackledge, Jim Kelly, Tony Eason and Ken O'Brien

"You know it was bad when the only person taking pictures in the locker room was my dad."
–Fred Smerlas, on his bleak days with the Buffalo Bills

THE SUPER BOWL
A Royal Flush of Questions

1. Who holds the Super Bowl record for the longest offensive play from scrimmage, an 85-yard touchdown reception in Super Bowl XXXVIII?

2. Who holds the career Super Bowl record for receiving yards, with 589?

3. Can you name the first franchise to win Super Bowls for two different cities?

4. Who was the first left-handed quarterback to win a Super Bowl?

5. What stadium hosted three of the first five Super Bowls?

6. Who is the youngest quarterback ever to win a Super Bowl?

7. This linebacker holds the record for the longest interception return in Super Bowl history.

---

*"Any person on the field can catch me from behind.
That includes the officials."*
—Hall of Fame receiver Fred Biletnikoff

8. The 49ers defeated the Bengals, 26-21, in Super Bowl XVI on January 24, 1982. It marked the first time a Super Bowl was played in the northern U.S. Do you know where?

9. Can you name the first African-American head coach to win a Super Bowl?

10. Who is the only coach in NFL history to win three Super Bowls within four years?

11. What team held its opponent to the fewest points in a single Super Bowl game?

12. This team has made the most consecutive trips to the Super Bowl, with 4.

13. Who holds the record for the longest run from scrimmage in Super Bowl history?

"Well, we do have a draw play here."
–Pat McInally, Cincinnati Bengals punter,
when asked if the art courses he took at Harvard
University helped him in the NFL

14. In the Pittsburgh Steelers' six Super Bowl victories, three wide receivers have been named the game's MVP. Who are they?

15. Can you name the Kansas City Chiefs owner who coined the phrase "Super Bowl"?

16. What quarterback holds the top three passing yardage totals for a single Super Bowl game?

17. The record for the most career playoff starts is held by the MVP of Super Bowl XXIII. Who is he?

18. Name the only team to make a Super Bowl appearance in the '70s, '80s, '90s, and in the first decade of the 21st century.

19. Jim Plunkett led the Raiders to two Super Bowl victories in the 1980's after being cut by which team?

"Munson hasn't done anything wrong. I'd bet my house on it."
—Joe Schmidt, Lions coach, after quarterback Bill Munson was asked to testify during a gambling inquiry

20. Can you name the only player to win the Super Bowl MVP as a kick returner?

21. Can you name the first father-son QB duo to each be on a Super Bowl championship team?

22. Who is the only quarterback to start in five Super Bowls?

23. Who is the oldest coach to win a Super Bowl?

24. Do you know the only two teams to meet each other in the Super Bowl three times?

25. Has a team ever played at a Super Bowl site which was also its home during the regular season?

THOUGHTS OF THE THRONE

"My mom says it's because I don't shave."

–Brett Favre, on why he didn't get as many commercial endorsements as fellow quarterback Troy Aikman

ANSWERS

1. Muhsin Muhammad, in Carolina's loss to New England
2. Jerry Rice, who played in four Super Bowls
3. The Raiders, for Oakland in 1977 and '81 and for L.A. in 1984
4. Ken Stabler
5. The Orange Bowl in Miami - Super Bowls II, III and V
6. Ben Roethlisberger, age 23, in Super Bowl XL
7. James Harrison - In Super Bowl XLIII, Harrison picked off the Cardinals' Kurt Warner and went 100 yards for a TD in the Steelers' win.
8. The Pontiac Silverdome in Michigan
9. Tony Dungy, in Super Bowl XLI, with the Colts (Mike Tomlin became the second with the Steelers in SB XLIII)
10. Bill Belichick, whose Patriots won three Super Bowls from 2001-04
11. Dallas Cowboys - In 1972, they defeated the Dolphins in Super Bowl VI, 24-3.
12. Buffalo Bills, from 1990-93

LAUGH-IN TIME-OUT

Q: How many Kansas City Chiefs does it take to change a flat tire?

A: One, unless it's a blowout...Then the whole team shows up.

13. Willie Parker, who ran 75 yards for a score in Pittsburgh's win over Seattle in Super Bowl XL
14. Lynn Swann (Super Bowl X), Hines Ward (XL) and Santonio Holmes (XLIII)
15. Lamar Hunt
16. Kurt Warner (414, 377 and 365 yards)
17. Jerry Rice
18. Pittsburgh Steelers
19. San Francisco 49ers
20. Desmond Howard, in Super Bowl XXXI
21. The Grieses – Bob with the Dolphins and Brian with the Broncos
22. John Elway
23. Dick Vermeil, age 63, when the Rams beat the Titans in Super Bowl XXXIV
24. Cowboys and Steelers (X, XII and XXX)
25. No

LAUGH-IN TIME-OUT

Q: What's a football player with good intuition called?

A: A hunchback

THE POST GAME SHOW

"I'm all for it."
–John McKay, Tampa Bay Buccaneers head coach, when asked
after another tough loss about his team's execution

— • —

"It's hard to believe, but the score started at 0-0."
–Dennis Green, Northwestern coach (later an NFL coach),
on his team being shut out by Iowa, 64-0

— • —

*"We can't run. We can't pass. We can't stop the run.
We can't stop the pass. We can't kick. Other than that, we're just not
a very good football team right now."*
–Bruce Coslet, Cincinnati Bengals coach

— • —

*"The good news is that our defense is giving up only one touchdown a
game. The bad news is that our offense is doing the same."*
–Bobby Bowden, Florida State coach

— • —

*"As a PR man, he is without equal. He could have made
Castro President of the United States."*
–Jim Murray, on Pete Rozelle

*"You're not going to win every game,
but I hate to prove it right off the bat."*
**–Jerry Burns, after losing his first game as
Vikings head coach**

— • —

*"I don't even go to self-service gasoline stations anymore because I
don't want to have to walk in and pay for it."*
**–Former Bengals coach Sam Wyche, when asked how he felt
about his team starting the season 0-5**

— • —

"Do we have to start at one?"
**–Tom Landry, when asked to rate the poor performance by
the Cowboys secondary on a scale of one to ten**

— • —

*"We're like a cross-eyed discus thrower. We don't win many medals,
but we keep the crowd loose."*
–Bill Curry, Kentucky football coach, describing his team

— • —

"If you play for the Lions, do you really need a ring finger?"
**–Mike Bianchi, after Detroit wide receiver Charles Rog-
ers dislocated his left ring finger while practicing**

"They say losing builds character. I have all the character I need."
–Ray Malavasi, former L.A. Rams coach

— • —

"I give the same halftime speech over and over. It works best when my players are better than the other coach's players."
–Chuck Mills

— • —

"My only feeling about superstition is that it's unlucky to be behind at the end of the game."
–Duffy Daugherty

— • —

"I'm really happy for Coach Cooper and the guys who've been around here for six or seven years, especially our seniors."
–Bob Hoying, Ohio State quarterback, after winning a Big Ten title

— • —

"When he runs the ball we use a lot of film."
–Vikings coach Dennis Green, on slow-footed quarterback Sean Salisbury

"I'll probably hear from mother about that."
–Texas coach Fred Akers, on playing every player on his team
except his own son Danny

— • —

*"I'd like to apologize to one person in particular, the man who won
the 'name the team' contest and got a lifetime pass."*
–Paul Martha, President of the USFL's Pittsburgh Maulers,
on the team folding after one year

— • —

"A stick of gum would have been enough."
–Fred Biletnikoff, Raiders wide receiver, as he was awarded
his Super Bowl XI MVP trophy

— • —

"Any one of 500 coaches could have won those Super Bowls."
–Cowboys owner Jerry Jones, on his team's consecutive Super
Bowl victories (XXVII & XXVIII)

— • —

*"If Howard Cosell had breakfast and dinner with
everybody he bragged about on* Monday Night Football,
he'd weigh 723 pounds."
–Joe Garagiola

"Anyone can have an off decade."
**–Larry Cole, Dallas Cowboys, after going 11 years
between scoring touchdowns**

— • —

"Our kicker had only one bad day last year- Saturday."
**–Tennessee Tech head coach Gary Darnell, after an
0-11 season the year before**

— • —

"I had the air-conditioning at my back."
**–Rusty Fricke, after kicking a 60-yard field goal in an Arena
Football League game**

— • —

*"That was just instinct. Kind of like running from the cops,
I guess you could say."*
**–Virginia's Marquis Weeks, after returning a 100-yard kickoff
against North Carolina**

— • —

*"You have to understand Thurman. If you didn't know him,
you'd think he was an idiot. We've known him two or three
years now, and we know he's an idiot."*
**–Will Wolford, teammate, on Bills running
back Thurman Thomas**

"Wehril's become one of my best receivers."
**–Roger Staubach, after Roger Wehril, defensive back for the
Rams, picked off three of his passes in one game**

— • —

"It's a once-in-a-lifetime thing that only happens every so often."
**–Randy Moss, explaining his no-look, over-the-shoulder
lateral to Moe Williams for a 59-yard TD**

— • —

*"Franco Harris faked me out so bad one time I got a
15-yard penalty for grabbing my own face mask."*
–D.D. Lewis

— • —

"If he were the sky, he would probably drop the Goodyear blimp."
**–Dan Jenkins, on Fred Solomon dropping
four passes in one game**

— • —

LAUGH-IN TIME-OUT

Q: How does Chad Ocho Cinco screw in a light bulb?

**A: He holds it up in the air and the world revolves
around him.**

EXTRA POINTS

"You ever see Rocky IV *when he goes to Russia?"*
**–Hines Ward, on the importance of home-field
advantage in the playoffs**

— • —

"I didn't vote for you, but you do have a nice suit on."
**–Don Meredith, during a visit from former Vice President
Spiro Agnew to the** *Monday Night Football* **booth**

— • —

*"One guy had a real low test score, so we decided to
go back and check with the interviews.
In one of them, he said he was raised by wolves."*
**–Dolphins coach Jimmy Johnson,
on a strange NFL draft situation**

— • —

"Contrary to public opinion, I have not worn that uniform before."
**–Jackie Slater, on wearing a nostalgic Rams jersey from the
1951 season, at age 40**

— • —

*"He said, 'Gosh, Dad, that means we're not going
to any more bowl games.'"*
**–Purdue football coach Jim Colleto, who was an assistant at
Arizona State and Ohio State, on his eleven-year-old son's
reaction after he was hired by the Boilermakers**

— • —

"He's like the Midas Muffler man. You can pay now or pay later."
–Mark Clayton, on
Dan Marino signing a five-year, $25-million contract

— • —

"Prom night was one of the worst nights of my life. My girlfriend
looked fantastic… The problem was, so did her date."
–Deion Sanders,
remembering his high school days

— • —

"He must shower in Vaseline."
–Lester Hayes, Raiders cornerback, on elusive Eagles quar-
terback Randall Cunningham

— • —

"When he didn't remember our anniversary, I knew he was OK."
–Lisa McCaffrey, on the concussion suffered by her husband,
Ed McCaffrey, of the Denver Broncos

— • —

"We have a motto that goes, 'To err is human.
To forgive is against league policy.'"
–Former Director of Personnel for the NFL, Mark Duncan

— • —

"If I drop dead tomorrow, at least I'll know I died in good health."
**–Former Houston Oilers coach Bum Phillips, after he passed
a physical**

— • —

*"I didn't quit football because I failed a drug test. I failed a drug test
because I was ready to quit football."*
–Ricky Williams

— • —

*"I told the administration I'd win the Big Ten championship
in two years if they'd let me do two things- spend all the
money I wanted to and cheat."*
**–Lee Corso, ESPN personality and former
Indiana University coach**

— • —

"There's a quote in The Bible *that says, 'Joseph died leaning on
his staff.' The same thing will be said about me when I pass away."*
–Lou Holtz

— • —

*"He'll be the first quarterback in history to play three quarters and
bill them for four."*
**–Jay Leno, *Tonight Show* host, about 49ers QB Steve Young
attending law school in the off-season**

— • —

*"There are two kinds of people in this world,
Notre Dame lovers and Notre Dame haters. And, quite frankly,
they're both a pain in the ass."*
–Dan Devine, former Notre Dame football coach

— • —

*"One of the major achievements of my life was to get more than $100
million in debt."*
**–Joe Robbie, talking about financing Miami's Joe Robbie
Stadium (now Dolphin Stadium)**

— • —

*"If a mugger in Central Park at night did what Richter does in the
afternoon, even the other muggers would turn him in."*
–An anonymous victim of Los Angeles linebacker Les Richter

— • —

"They don't like my overhand delivery."
–Bubba Smith, after being banned from bowling alleys

— • —

*"He's great to the old guys.
He's got one trainer just to treat varicose veins."*
–Alex Karras, on Redskins coach George Allen

— • —

"The really scary thing is that some of these people work for the government."
–Joe Jacoby, on "Hog" supporters who show up at Redskins games wearing pig snouts

— • —

"It's kind of difficult to introduce a guy you hope gets the flu every week."
–Cowboys backup quarterback Gary Hogeboom, introducing Danny White, the starting quarterback, at a roast

— • —

"We were the only team in pro football whose team picture showed both a front and side view."
–Ken Stabler, on the Raiders bad boy image

— • —

"We had many discussions, but I wasn't listening."
–Don Meredith, on talking with Tom Landry

— • —

"It's like saving up all your life to move out of a grubby tenement and then finding out you've moved next door."
–Jim Cadle, on moving from center to guard after 11 seasons in the NFL

— • —

"We have a lot of stars, just no one you've ever heard of."
–49ers GM Terry Donahue

— • —

"Coach Lombardi is very fair. He treats us all like dogs."
–Henry Jordan

— • —

"With so many Super Bowl rings, maybe they'll all retire and go into the jewelry business."
–John McKay, on the Steelers' Super Bowl wins

— • —

"I think all uniforms look nice if you've got good players in 'em."
–Bill Parcells

— • —

"Don't bother reading it, kid- everybody gets killed in the end."
–Peter Gent of the Cowboys, telling a rookie not to read the team's playbook

— • —

"I've dated girls who were far better looking than the quality of girls who should be going out with me."
–Cris Collinsworth, on some of the perks that came with being an NFL player

— • —

"I don't like the idea of practicing six days to play one."
–Robin Yount, baseball Hall of Famer, on the game of football

— • —

"The greatest name in football."
–Alex Karras, on Browns wide receiver Fair Hooker

— • —

"The road to Easy Street goes through the sewer."
–John Madden

— • —

"If I were the NFL commissioner, I'd put all the offensive linemen in jail for 30 days or make them spend one week with Mike Ditka."
–Dexter Manley

— • —

"I'd just like to put it behind me."
–Quarterback Peyton Manning, when asked about the alleged "mooning" of teammates in front of a female trainer

— • —

"Probably The Beatles' White Album."
–Steve Largent, wide receiver, on which record he will cherish the most

— • —

"Because I'm still 30 credits short of getting my degree."
–Jim Zorn, describing why he was surprised when his alma
mater, Cal Poly, contacted him about giving a keynote address

— • —

"Hopefully, that will get done in time, and if not, shortly thereafter."
–Steelers coach Bill Cowher, on the chances of signing 2004
first round pick Ben Roethlisberger

— • —

"I haven't read it yet."
–Johnny Unitas, when asked about his autobiography

— • —

*"Ryan Leaf threw fourteen touchdown passes in his
NFL career and grossed $13 million. Bust? Hardly. I'd say he got
the most out of his abilities."*
–Mike Bianchi

— • —

"It's like finding out your mother-in-law has a twin sister."
–New York Giants radio color commentator Dick Lynch, on
the Green Bay Packers trading for receiver John Jefferson to
go along with their other star receiver, James Lofton

— • —

*"You go to the Pro Bowl and people looking at your
T-shirt ask you what your average is.
They think you're part of the Pro Bowlers' Tour."*
**–Redskins guard R.C. Thielemann, on making football's
all-star game**

— • —

"I may be dumb, but I'm not stupid."
–Terry Bradshaw

— • —

*"Let's face it, you have to have a slightly recessive gene that has a
little something to do with the brain to go out on the football field and
beat your head against other human beings on a daily basis."*
–Tim Green

— • —

*"You have to play this game like someone just hit
your mother with a two-by-four."*
–Dan Birdwell

— • —

*"They say a tie is like kissing your sister. I guess that is
better than kissing your brother."*
–Lou Holtz

— • —

"It's almost like life. Just when it begins to look rosy, somebody will intercept a pass and run ninety yards against you."
–John Facenda, former NFL Films narrator, on the game of football

— • —

"Statistics always remind me of the fellow who drowned in a river whose average depth was only three feet."
–Woody Hayes

— • —

"We have a lot of players in their first year. Some of them are also in their last year."
–Bill Walsh, 49ers coach

— • —

"My job has become decoy. I draw the attack and the other guys make the plays. I should show up painted like a duck."
–Howie Long, defensive lineman for the 1984 Super Bowl Raiders

— • —

"That's kind of ironic, don't you think? Here's a guy who was an All-American football star in college. Then when he gets a job, he spends 30 years sitting on a bench."
–Jay Leno, on Byron "Whizzer" White, a top running back in his day and later a Supreme Court Justice

— • —

"Not only is he ambidextrous, but he can throw with either hand."
–Duffy Daugherty

— • —

*"A hotel operator called and said I had been indicted.
I panicked and said, 'For what?'"*
**–John Mackey, on notification of his "induction" to the Pro
Football Hall of Fame**

— • —

*"Dan and I had our ups and downs. Once we didn't speak for two
weeks. I didn't think it was right to interrupt him."*
–Bob Costas, on Dan Dierdorf

— • —

"It's an internal matter."
**–Bill Walsh, 49ers coach, on reports of Russ Francis missing
practice because of a stomach problem**

— • —

*"If you play one regular-season game in the National Football
League, you will never, ever, be normal physically."*
–John Madden

— • —

"When other players started asking me for permission to date my daughter."
–Y.A. Tittle, Hall of Fame quarterback, when asked about his first thoughts of retiring

— • —

"You come out hurting all over, and what didn't hurt didn't work."
–Jim Otto, Raiders center, on dealing with "Mean" Joe Greene

— • —

"After three failed marriages, I know what it's like to be replaced."
–Terry Bradshaw, on Lions QB Joey Harrington constantly falling out of favor with the club

— • —

"Knute Rockne liked 'bad losers.' He said 'good losers' lose too often."
–George Allen

— • —

"A good football coach needs a patient wife, a loyal dog and a great quarterback - but not necessarily in that order."
–Bud Grant

— • —

"They say two things happen when you get older. One is you forget things. And I can't remember what the other is right now."
–Marv Levy, speaking as the new Bills general manager at the age of 80

— • —

"He's like a diner. He's open all the time."
–Jimmy the Greek, on former Cardinals wideout Roy Green

— • —

"My biggest problems are defensive linemen and offensive alumni."
–Bo Schembechler, on Michigan State boosters

— • —

"A good rule in life is to never become too important to do your own laundry."
–Barry Sanders

— • —

"Sure, I've got one. It's a perfect 20-20."
–Cowboys running back Duane Thomas, when asked about his IQ

— • —

"It was like the Pope not being allowed to say Mass."
–Chris Spielman, Bills linebacker, on not being able to work out for a couple of months because of a neck injury

— • —

"The next time I see a doctor it better be for an autopsy."
–Dolphins linebacker A.J. Duhe, after his fifth operation in 18 months

— • —

"I can't even count to ten in English."
–Steelers WR Lee Mays, when asked on Media Day before Super Bowl XL if he could count to ten in a foreign language

— • —

"I never graduated from the University of Iowa, but I was only there for two terms – Truman's and Eisenhower's."
–Alex Karras

— • —

"People say somewhere in the first round- maybe even higher."
–Craig "Ironhead" Heyward, on where he would be drafted

— • —

"Jimmy Brown was the finest all-around athlete I ever saw — he was a jock-of-all trades."
–Jon Weber

— • —

"I'm probably about a 4.9 normally, but when a 280-pound guy is chasing me, I'm a 4.6."
–John Elway, on his speed in the 40-yard dash

— • —

"I didn't care too much for that. It's kind of embarrassing if you're a pitcher."
–Falcons coach Dan Reeves, on having the nickname "Homerun" when he played college baseball

— • —

"Two out of three ain't bad."
–Tex Schramm, then-Dallas President, after hearing that Cowboys running back Duane Thomas had called him "a liar, a thief and a crook"

— • —

"They're married to them."
– Cincinnati coach Forrest Gregg, on why he permitted Bengals players to sleep with their wives before the Super Bowl

— • —

THE BATHROOM LIBRARY

The Bathroom Baseball Book

•

The Bathroom Bloopers Book

•

The Bathroom Football Book

•

The Bathroom Funny Pages

•

The Bathroom Game Book

•

The Bathroom Golf Book

•

The Bathroom Joke Book

•

The Bathroom LOL Book

•

The Bathroom Sports Pages

•

The Bathroom Sports Quiz Book

•

The Bathroom Trivia Book

•

The Bathroom Trivia Digest